THE ESSENTIAL COLLECTION

SCHUMANN

GOLD

Published by
Chester Music Limited
14-15 Berners Street, London W1T 3LJ, UK.

Exclusive Distributors:
Music Sales Limited
Distribution Centre, Newmarket Road, Bury St Edmunds, Suffolk IP33 3YB, UK.
Music Sales Corporation
180 Madison Avenue, 24th Floor, New York NY 10016, USA.
Music Sales Pty Limited
Units 3-4, 17 Willfox Street, Condell Park, NSW 2200, Australia.

Order No. CH78826
ISBN 978-1-78038-299-9
This book © Copyright 2013 by Chester Music.

Music engraved by Note-orious Productions Limited.
Compiled by Quentin Thomas.
CD Project Manager: Ruth Power.
CD recorded and produced by Mutual Chord Studio, Guangzhou, China.

Book printed and CD manufactured in the EU.

Previously available as book only CH66863.

Your Guarantee of Quality:
As publishers, we strive to produce every book to the highest commercial standards.
The music has been carefully designed to minimise awkward page turns
and to make playing from it a real pleasure.
Particular care has been given to specifying acid-free, neutral-sized
paper made from pulps which have not been elemental chlorine bleached.
This pulp is from farmed sustainable forests and was produced
with special regard for the environment.
Throughout, the printing and binding have been planned to ensure a sturdy,
attractive publication which should give years of enjoyment.
If your copy fails to meet our high standards, please inform us and we will gladly replace it.
www.musicsales.com

CHESTER MUSIC
part of The Music Sales Group
London / New York / Paris / Sydney / Copenhagen / Berlin / Madrid / Hong Kong / Tokyo

The Happy Farmer

from Album For The Young, Op.68

Composed by Robert Schumann

The Reaper's Song

from Album For The Young, Op.68

Composed by Robert Schumann

Little Study

from Album For The Young, Op.68

Composed by Robert Schumann

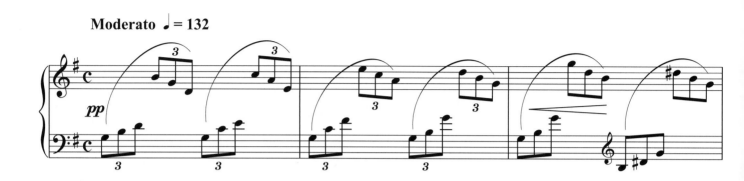

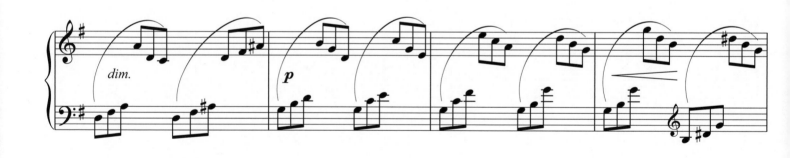

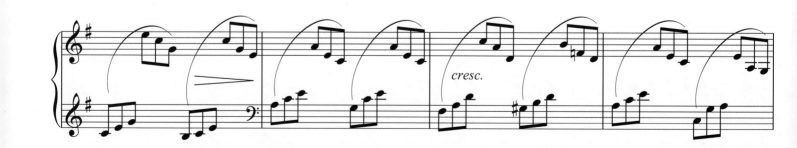

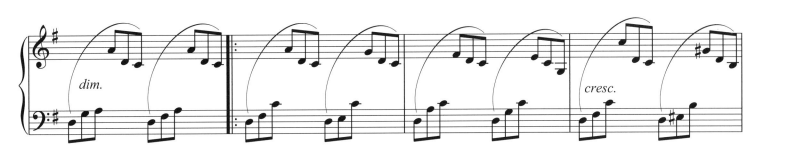

rit.   a tempo

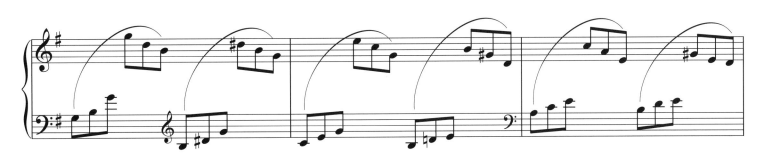

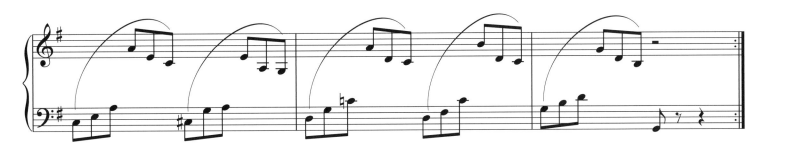

Molto Lento
from Album For The Young, Op.68

Composed by Robert Schumann

The Wild Horseman

from Album For The Young, Op.68

Composed by Robert Schumann

Phantasietanz
(Fantasy Dance)
from Album Leaves, Op.124

Composed by Robert Schumann

Sehr rasch

Lied Ohne Ende
(Song Without End)
from Album Leaves, Op.124

Composed by Robert Schumann

2.

Leidenschaftlicher

Tempo I

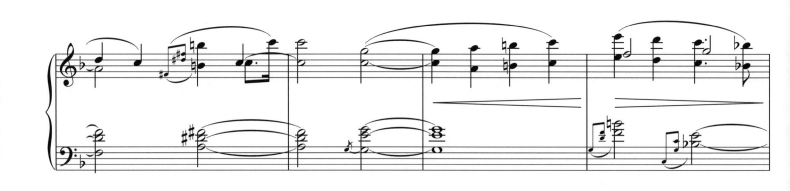

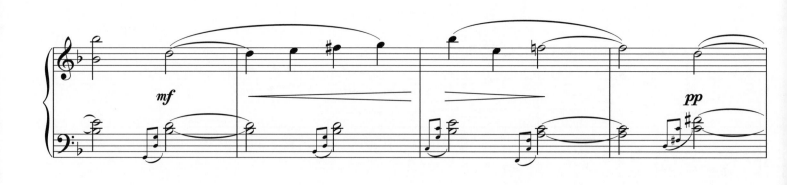

Romanze
from Album Leaves, Op.124
Composed by Robert Schumann

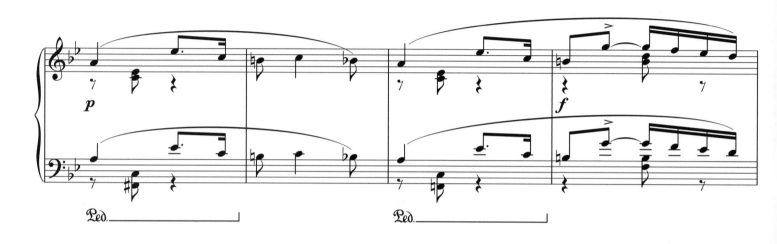

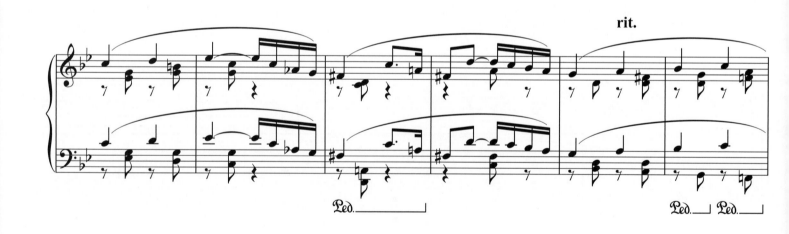

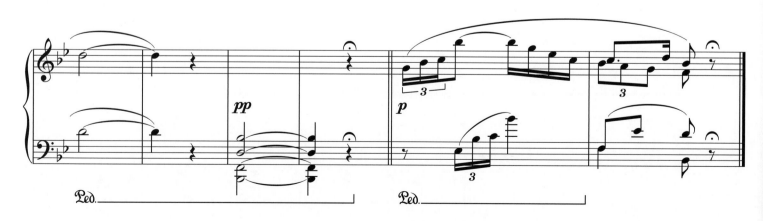

Chiarina

from Carnaval, Op.9

Composed by Robert Schumann

20

21

Chopin
from Carnaval, Op.9
Composed by Robert Schumann

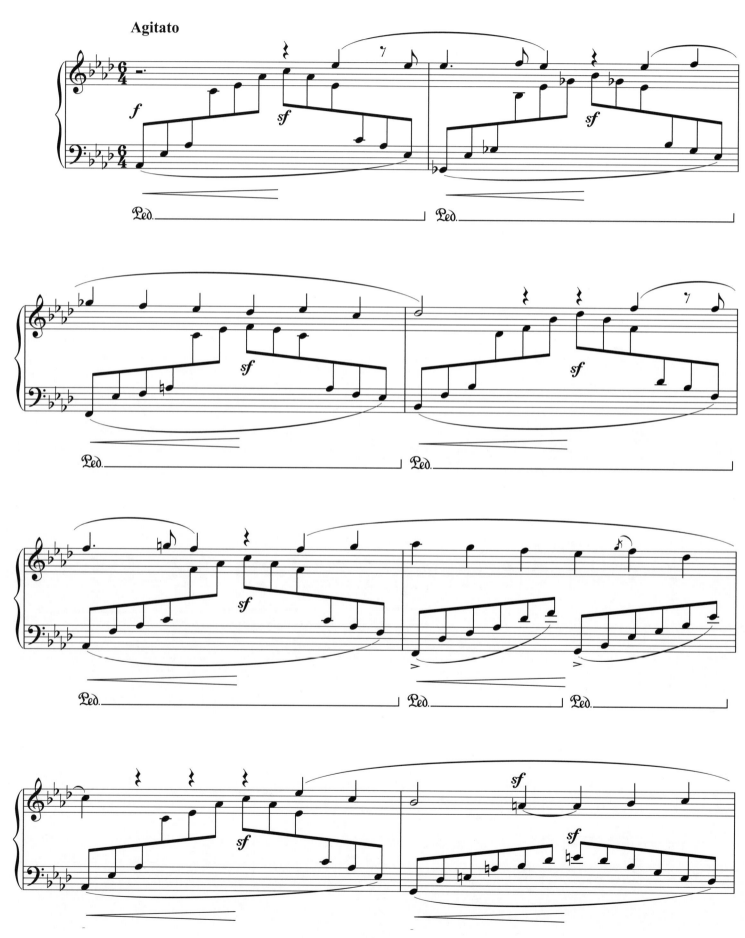

rit.

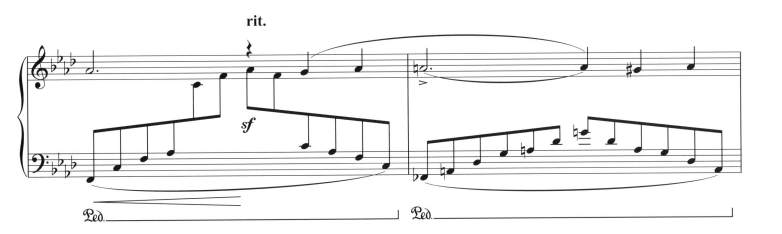

a tempo

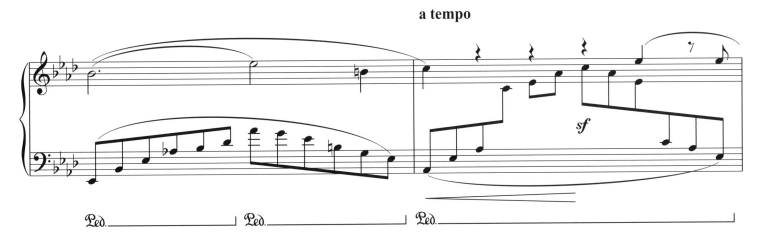

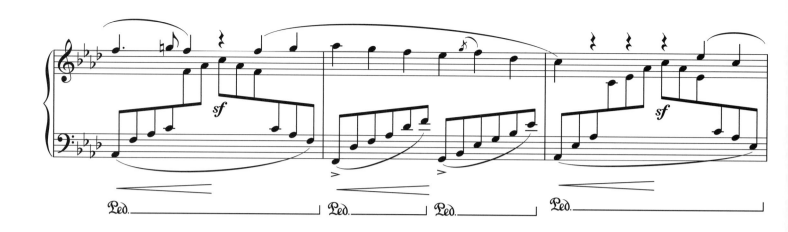

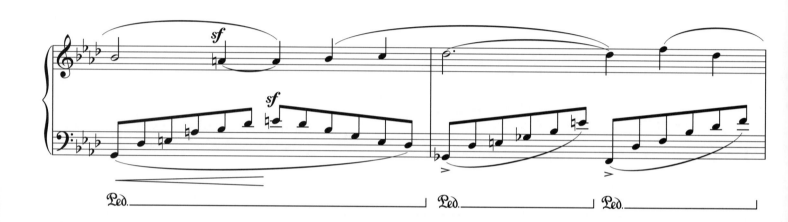

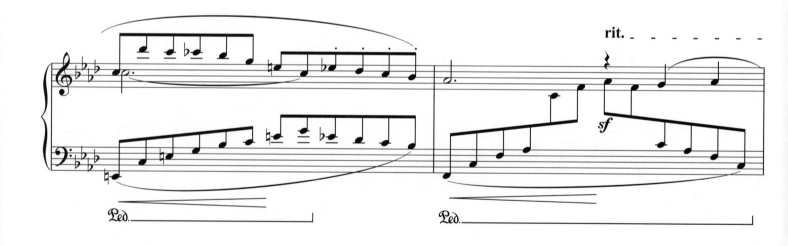

March
from Coloured Leaves, Op.99

Composed by Robert Schumann

Molto sostenuto

Trio

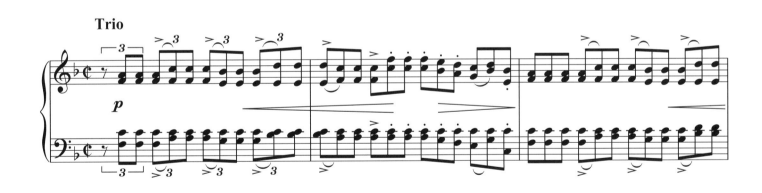

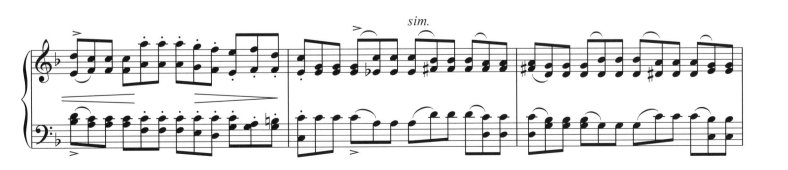

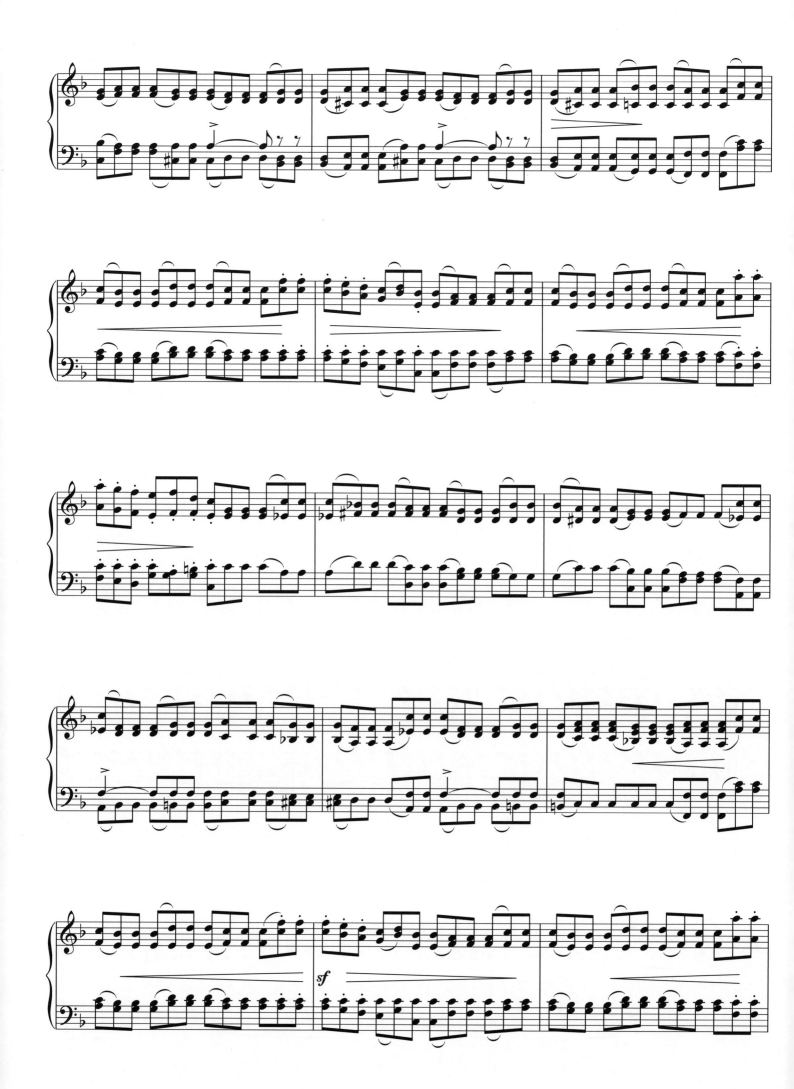

28

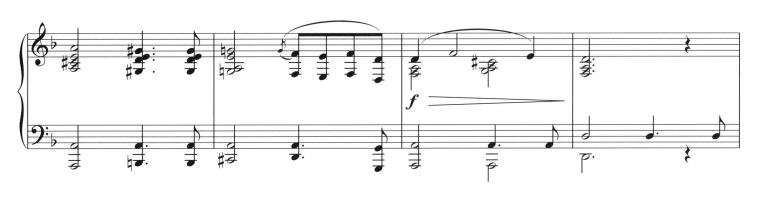

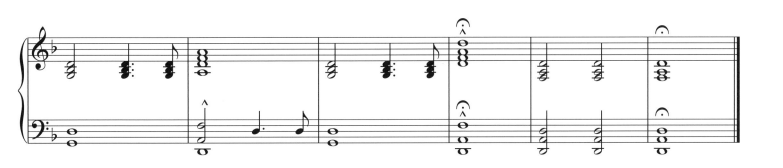

Novellette
from Coloured Leaves, Op.99

Composed by Robert Schumann

Lebhaft
(Spirited)
from Davidsbündler / 18 Character Pieces, Op.6

Composed by Robert Schumann

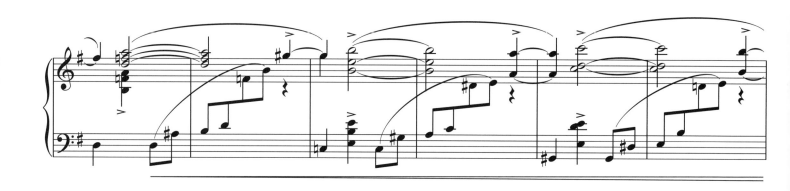

rit.   Im tempo

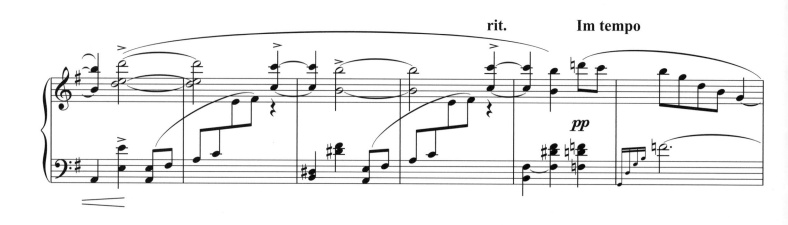

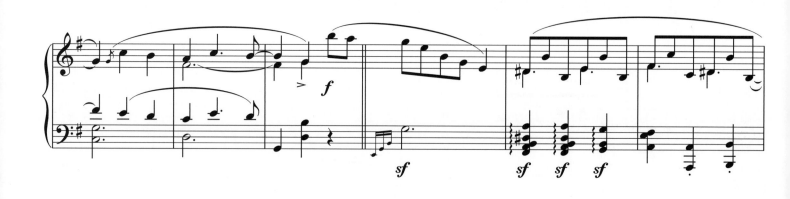

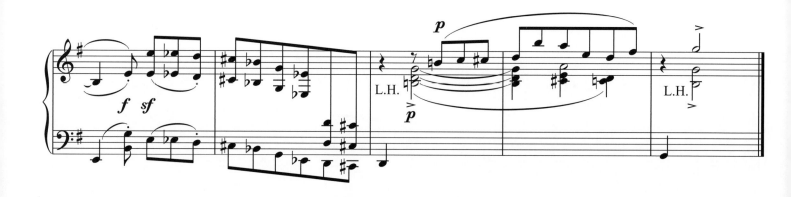

Innig
(Heartfelt)
from Davidsbündler / 18 Character Pieces, Op.6

Composed by Robert Schumann

rit.　　　　　　Im tempo

rit.　　　　　　Im tempo

Mit Humor
(With Humour)

from Davidsbündler / 18 Character Pieces, Op.6

Composed by Robert Schumann

Mit Humor ♩. = 60

Schneller

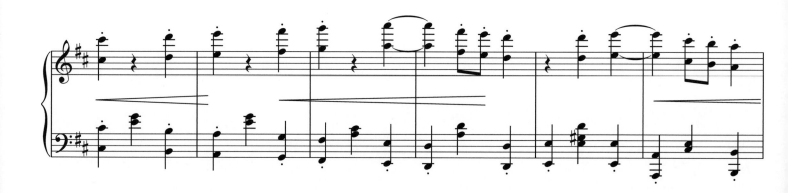

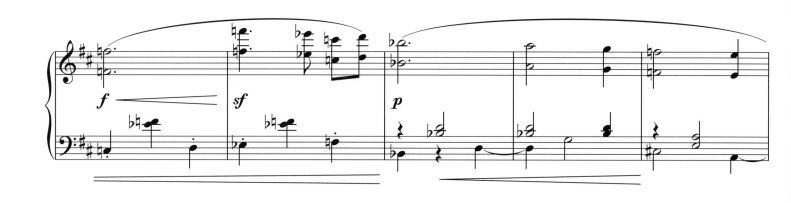

rit.

Tempo I

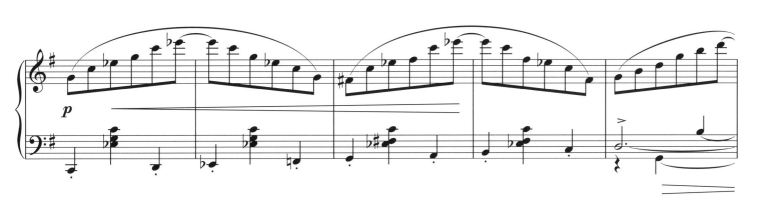

Warum?

(Why?)

from Fantasy Pieces, Op.12

Composed by Robert Schumann

Langsam und zart

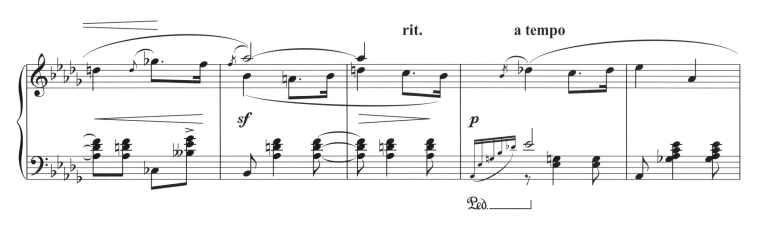

Friendly Landscape
from Forest Scenes, Op.82

Composed by Robert Schumann

Romanze

from Imaginary Pictures, Op.26

Composed by Robert Schumann

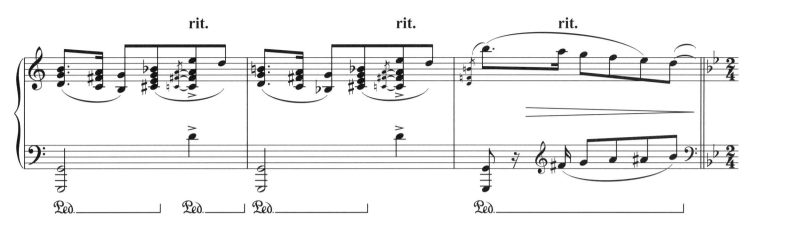

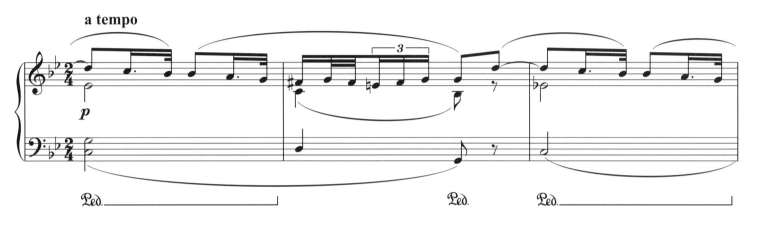

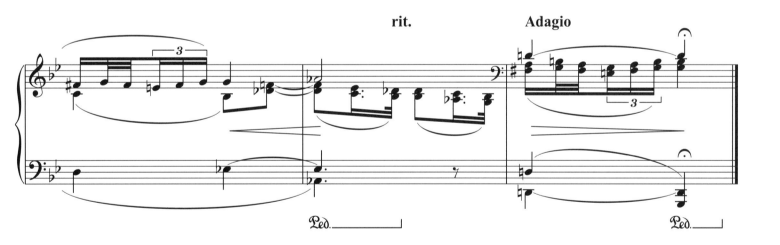

Piece No.1
from Night Pieces, Op.23
Composed by Robert Schumann

Rather slow, often restrained ♩ = 100

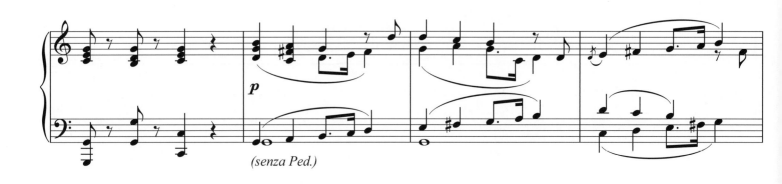

From Foreign Lands And People

from Scenes From Childhood, Op.15

Composed by Robert Schumann

Child Falling Asleep
from Scenes From Childhood, Op.15

Composed by Robert Schumann

Theme With Variations
from Sonatas For The Young, Op.118

Composed by Robert Schumann

Sonata For Children, Op.118, No.1
(1st Movement)

Composed by Robert Schumann

Theme in E♭ Major

Composed by Robert Schumann

Leise, innig

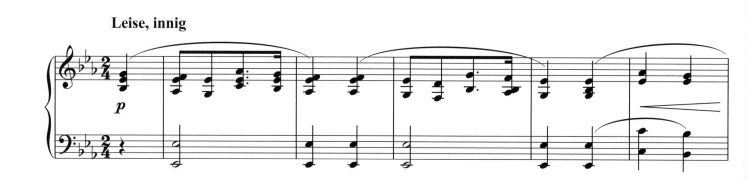

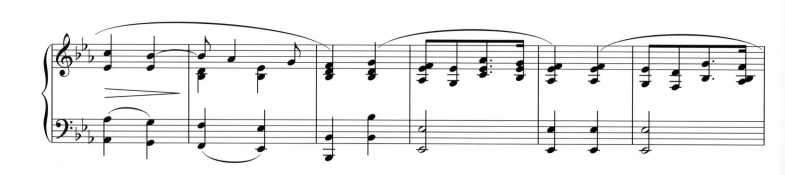

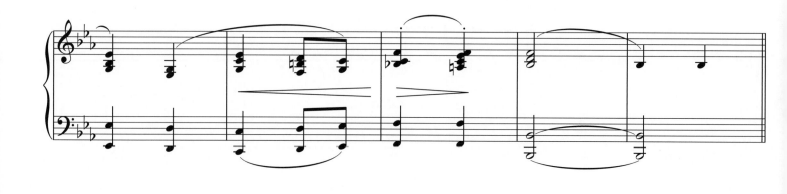

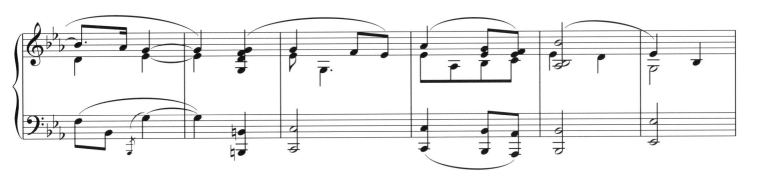

Träumerei

from Scenes From Childhood, Op.15

Composed by Robert Schumann

An Die Sterne
(To The Stars)

Composed by Robert Schumann   Arranged by Quentin Thomas

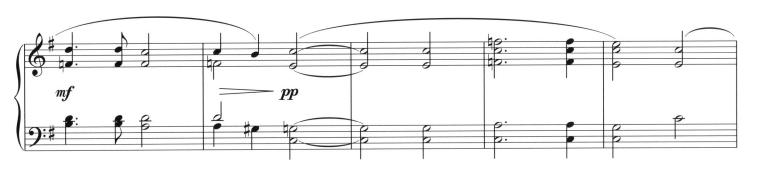

Widmung
(Wedding Dedication)
from Myrthen, Op.25

Composed by Robert Schumann   Arranged by Quentin Thomas

Langsam

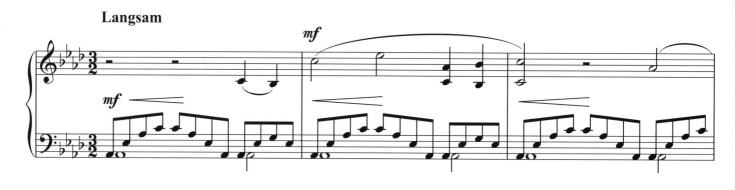

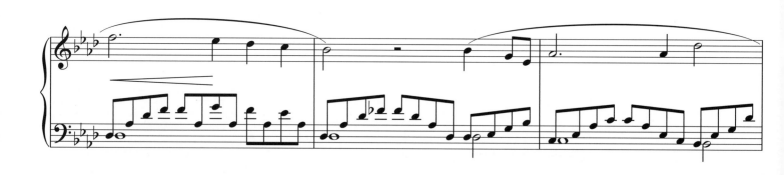

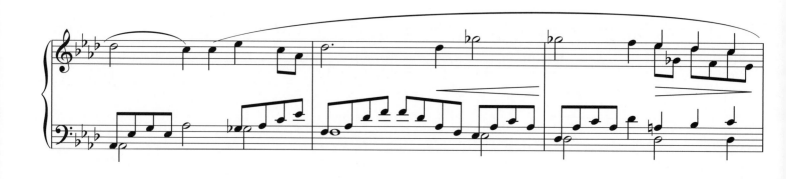

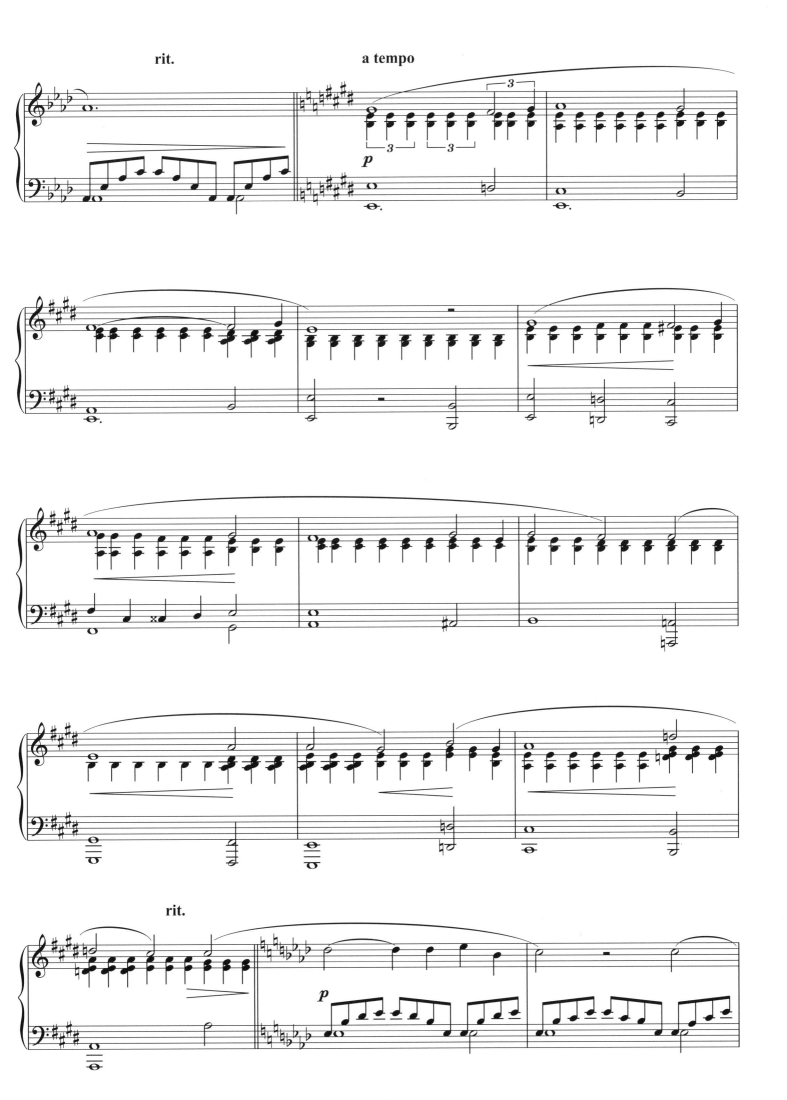

Du Bist Wie Eine Blume
(Sweet As Any Flower)
from Myrthen, Op.25

Composed by Robert Schumann   Arranged by Quentin Thomas

Stille Thränen
(Hidden Tears)
from 12 Gedichte, Op.35

Composed by Robert Schumann   Arranged by Quentin Thomas

Sehr langsam

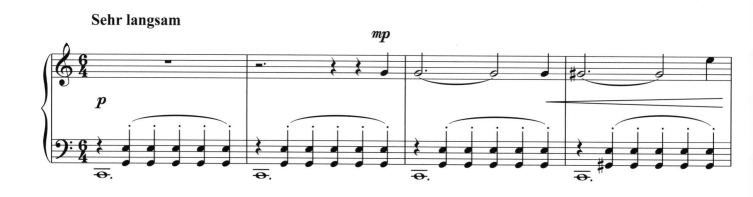

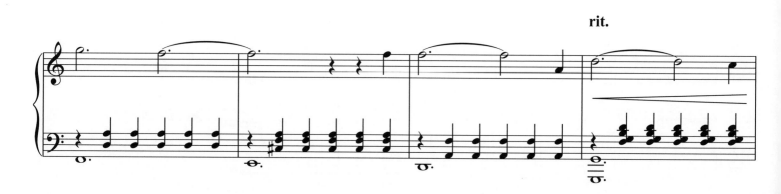

a tempo

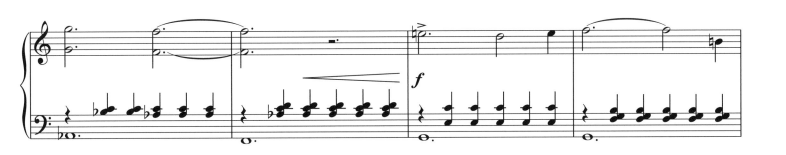

rit.

rit.   Adagio

Ich Will Meine Seele Tauchen
(I Will Immerse My Soul)
from Dichterliebe, Op.48

Composed by Robert Schumann   Arranged by Quentin Thomas

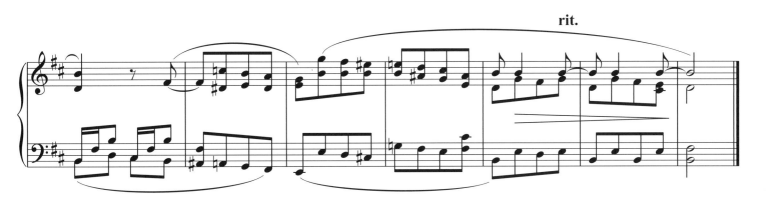

Ich Grolle Nicht
(I'm Not Grumbling)
from Dichterliebe, Op.48

Composed by Robert Schumann   Arranged by Quentin Thomas

Nicht schnell

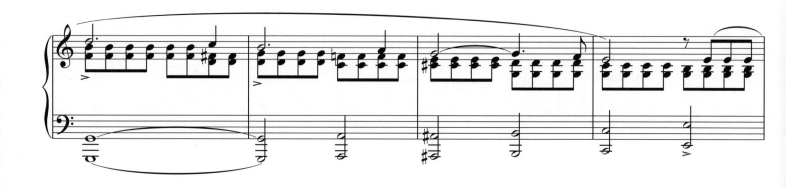

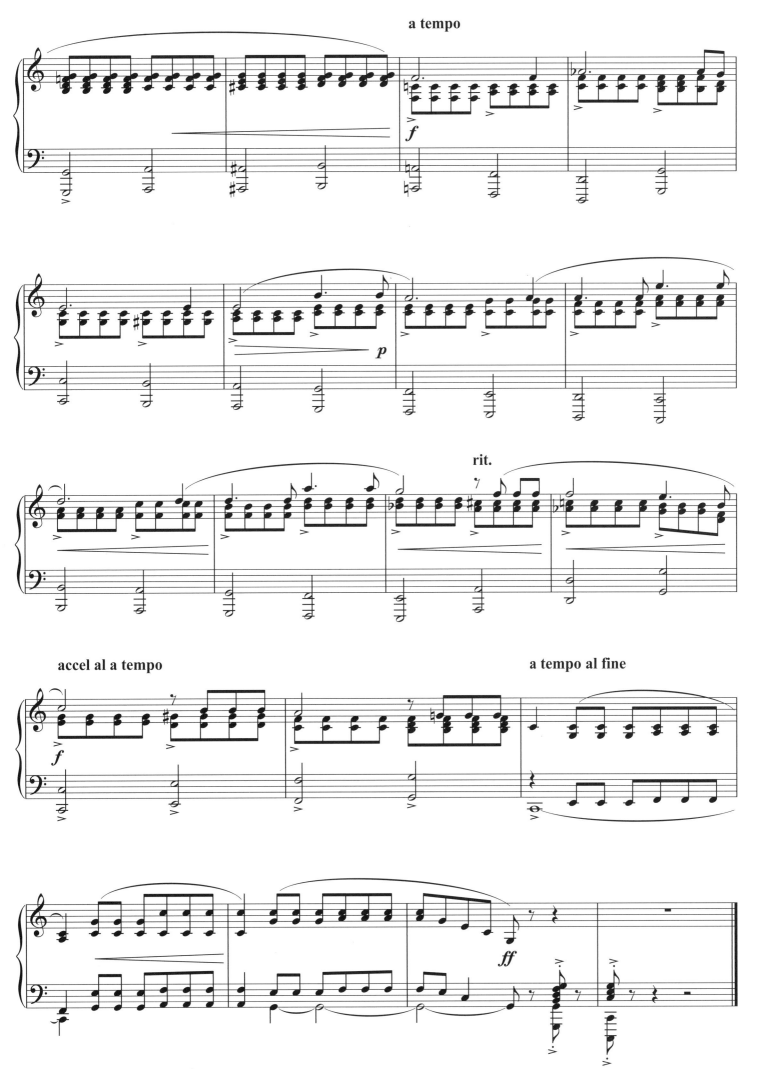

Im Wunderschönen Monat Mai
(In The Wonderful Month Of May)
from Dichterliebe, Op.48

Composed by Robert Schumann   Arranged by Quentin Thomas

rit.

Er Und Sie
(Him And Her)

Composed by Robert Schumann   Arranged by Quentin Thomas

Nicht Schnell

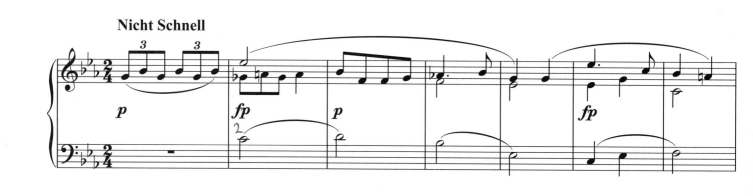

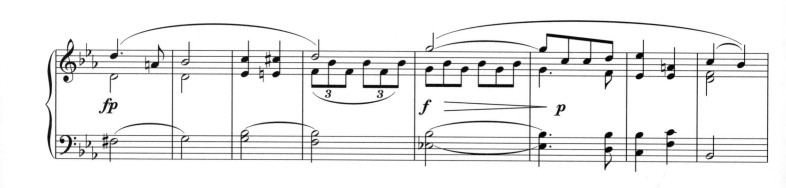

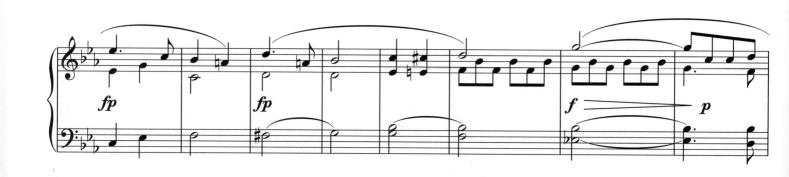

allargando   a tempo

String Quartet in A Major, Op.41, No.3

(2nd Movement: Un poco adagio)

Composed by Robert Schumann   Arranged by Quentin Thomas

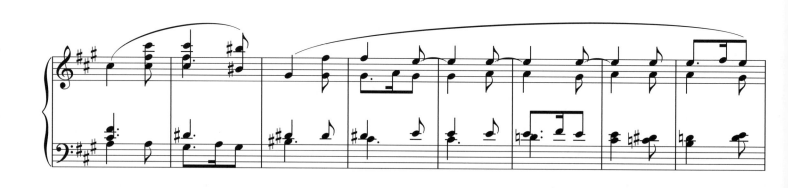

Piano Quartet in E♭ Major, Op.47

(3rd Movement: Andante cantabile)

Composed by Robert Schumann   Arranged by Quentin Thomas

92

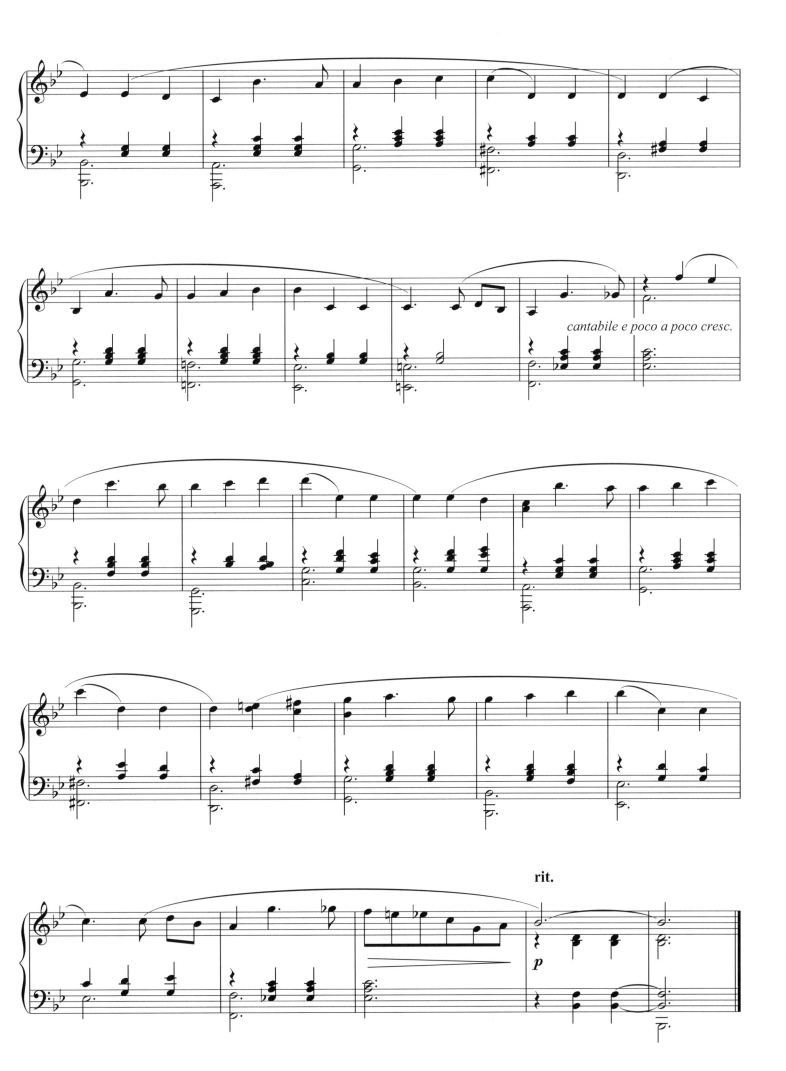

cantabile e poco a poco cresc.

rit.

p

Symphony No.2 in C Major, Op.61

(3rd Movement: Adagio espressivo)

Composed by Robert Schumann   Arranged by Quentin Thomas

Adagio espressivo (♪ = 76)

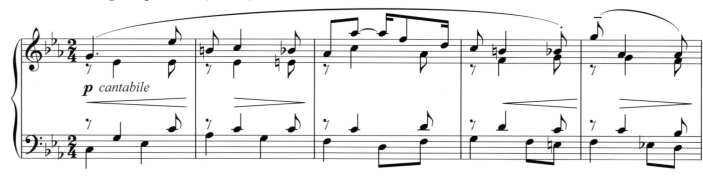

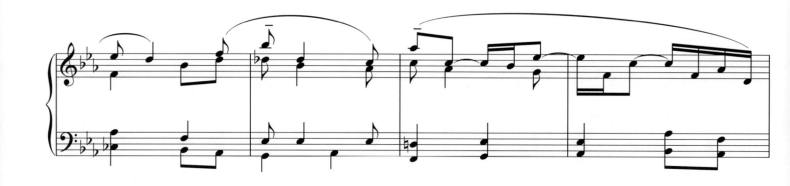

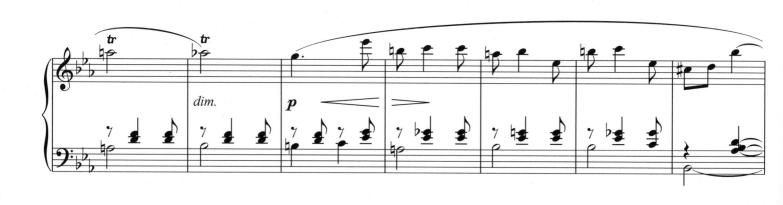